SCOOBY-DOO!™

Welcome!

Join Scooby-Doo and the Mystery, Inc. gang for lots of crazy creative projects to make and do.

Each project is made from everyday items that you find around the house. All you have to do is follow the simple steps to create your own scooby-dooper creepy crafts!
So turn the page and join the gang for loads of spooky activities and ghoulish giggles. Zoinks! Like, it's gonna be a whole lotta fun, man!

Contents

Editor: Kate Rhead, Designers: Vicki Turner & Ant Gardner,
Artist: Paul Gamble, Craft makers: Kate Tompsett & Angela Hart

GET THE MESSAGE!

Create this Scooby-Doo blackboard and the grooviest of Great Danes will remind you of all your important memos!

1 Draw the shape of Scooby's head and body on a large piece of card. Start by drawing a circle for his body, then add an oblong shape for his head. Add two triangles for his arms and sketch in the shape of his feet and legs.

2 Now add some detail to his shape. Sketch in his ears and face. Add some definition to the shape of his arms and body. Use the picture of Scooby to help you. Once you are happy with the shape, cut it out!

3 Give your memo board a cool 3-D look! Cut out the shape of Scooby's muzzle, collar and his left foot from card and glue them in position on the memo board.

JINKIES! THIS IS AN EXCELLENT WAY TO KEEP NOTE OF ALL THOSE IMPORTANT REMINDERS!

4

SCOOBY snacks

YOU WILL NEED:
Thick card,
blackboard paint,
paints and a paintbrush
scissors,
PVA glue,
newspaper.

SCOOBY RULES!

4 Cover the whole memo board with 2-3 layers of PVA glue and newspaper, and leave it to dry.

5 Paint Scooby with brown paint. Add the black spots on his coat and paint the details on his face. Now paint a large black circle on his tummy using blackboard paint. Once it is dry, use coloured chalk to scribble all your Scooby-doodles on his tummy!

woof!

woof!

Haunted Mansion!

R.I.P. 1

Take the large cardboard box and cut two card rectangles to fit inside it. Tape them into place - these will make the floors.

R.I.P. 2

Cut a rectangle of card so that it can slot inside the top floor and create two rooms. Before you fix it in place, cut a rectangle out of the card to make a doorway. Now tape the wall into place.

R.I.P. 3

Glue a large card rectangle to the bottom of the box. Use this as a base for attaching lots of balls of rolled up newspaper. These will become rocks and the bottom floor of the house will be a spooky underground cellar! Make a secret tunnel by sticking half of a cardboard tube to the base, and build the newspaper up around it.

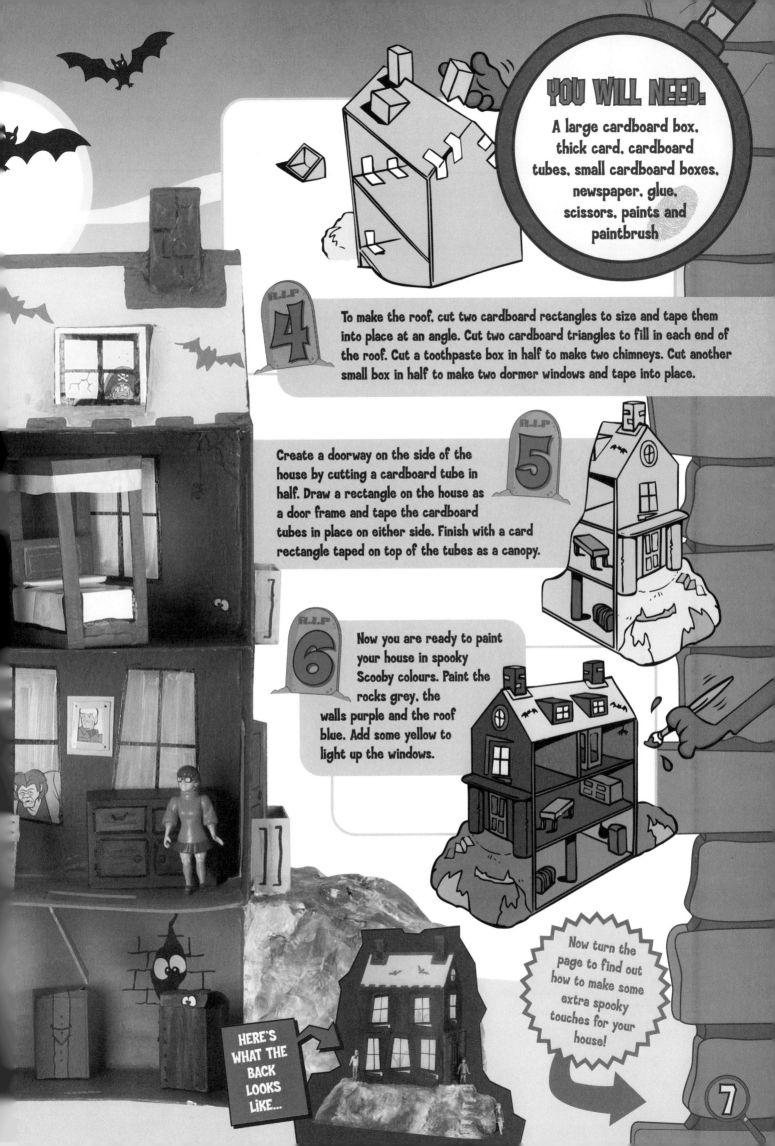

4 To make the roof, cut two cardboard rectangles to size and tape them into place at an angle. Cut two cardboard triangles to fill in each end of the roof. Cut a toothpaste box in half to make two chimneys. Cut another small box in half to make two dormer windows and tape into place.

5 Create a doorway on the side of the house by cutting a cardboard tube in half. Draw a rectangle on the house as a door frame and tape the cardboard tubes in place on either side. Finish with a card rectangle taped on top of the tubes as a canopy.

6 Now you are ready to paint your house in spooky Scooby colours. Paint the rocks grey, the walls purple and the roof blue. Add some yellow to light up the windows.

HERE'S WHAT THE BACK LOOKS LIKE...

Now turn the page to find out how to make some extra spooky touches for your house!

7

Haunted Mansion Continued!

Now you have created your haunted mansion, you need to add some really spooky touches! Here are some handy hints on how to decorate your house.

Room with a view!

Add some balconies to the side of your house. Cut a door shape into the outside wall. Cut a rectangle of card and fold three of the sides in to make a narrow box shape. Tape the three sides into position at the bottom of the window to create a balcony for your action figures to stand on!

Trap door terror!

Create a terrifying trap door leading to the cellar. Use a pencil to draw some floorboards on the floor. Then draw a square in the middle of the floor and cut out three sides of it. You can even write 'Thud!' on the floor below to show where your victims will land!

Freaky Furniture!

Decorate the interior of the house with some crazy furniture. Use small cardboard boxes to make wardrobes, chests and old trunks. Paint them brown and add details in black. Draw some spooky eyes and ghoulish hands on paper colour them in, cut them out and stick them to the furniture to add some Scooby scariness!

Weird Windows!

Draw some rectangles on the back of the house and paint them yellow to give them a ghostly glow. Add the shadows of some ghoulish spooks in orange. Outline the windows in black.

BAGS OF FUN!

Like, these monster masks are totally hairy scary and they are, like, really easy peasy to make!

There are all kinds of creepy creatures you can make into a mask! Use silver paint to create a robot - don't forget to add a cardboard antennae to the top of his head!

1 You will need a sturdy brown paper bag - the kind used for takeaway food is perfect. Cut off any handles, and make sure that it fits on your head.

2 To create a Frankenstein's monster mask, cut out and stick on cardboard ears and a bolt for your monster's neck.

3 Paint one side of the bag white, to make designing your mask easier. Draw on features with a pencil. Paint your Frankenstein's monster with green and black paint, and add red scars. Paint his bolt silvery grey.

4 Cut small peep holes in your bag mask so that you can see where you are going!

Scooby Hint!

These masks make a great activity for a spooky party. Give each guest a paper bag and ask them to create their own monster. The gooniest ghoul created wins a prize!

IN THE FRAME

This spooky portrait with moving eyes is an essential in any haunted house! Follow the steps to make your own spookerific portrait!

1 Draw the shape of the frame on thick cardboard. Make the rounded corners by drawing around a cup. Once you are happy with the shape, cut it out. Cut the centre out as well.

2 Roll up strips of newspaper into sausages and position around the frame to make ornate swirls. Cover it in a layer of newspaper and glue and leave to dry.

3 Measure the centre of the frame and draw a rectangle the same size on a piece of card. Now draw a picture of someone's head and shoulders on the card. Paint the picture and cut the eyes out.

Scooby Hint!
You could even use a photograph of a friend for your portrait! Photocopy it, blow it up to size and tape it in place.

4 Tape the picture in place behind the frame. Now tape two thin strips of card on to the back of the frame to make runners for the moving eyes.

5 Cut a strip of card and slot it into the runners on the back of the frame. You should be able to slide it back and forth. Turn the frame back over and draw the eyes in the centre of the card strip. Now pull the card to the left and right and the spooky eyes will follow you wherever you go!

Put your foot in it!

Put your best paw forward with these fun Scooby-Doo paws! Ree-hee-hee!

1

Stick the lid of the box to the base with sticky tape. Cut a hole in the top of the box for your foot to fit through.

2

Cut out the two back corners of the box to shape the heel of the foot. Cut squares of card and tape into position to cover the holes.

3

Partly blow up four of the balloons and use sticky tape to fix them to the front of the box. These will make Scooby's toes!

4

Roll up a sausage of kitchen roll and tape around the hole on the top of the box. Now cover the whole box in torn-up newspaper and glue and leave it to dry.

5

Now paint the foot brown. Repeat steps 1-5 with the other shoe box to give you two fantastic Scooby paws to wear!

13

BATS ABOUT IT!

This scary bat will add some high-flying spookiness to your bedroom!

1 Stuff the cardboard tube with old newspaper. Tape a larger ball of newspaper to one end to make the bat's head. Cover the whole bat in torn up newspaper and glue and leave to dry.

2 Cut two wing shapes from a piece of card. Cut two small triangles for ears and two small feet. To attach the wings, make four holes as shown in the diagram. Make two holes on each wing and four holes on the bat's body.

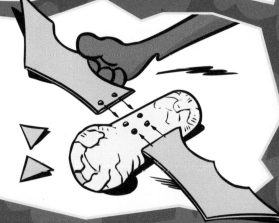

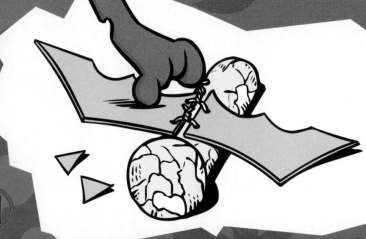

3 Thread a length of pipe cleaner through one of the holes on the wing, through two of the holes on the body and one of the holes on the other wing. Twist the pipe cleaner together loosely to secure the wing in place. Repeat for the other holes.

4 Tape the feet and ears into place. Now you can paint the bat black. Don't forget to add eyes, nose, a mouth and fangs.

YOU WILL NEED:
Short cardboard tube, newspaper, thick card, glue and sticky tape, paints and paintbrush, elastic, and a bead

5 To make the flying mechanism, make two small holes at the end of each wing. Thread a piece of elastic through one hole, over the bat's body and through the hole on the other wing. Secure with knots underneath each wing.

Attach a length of elastic to the underside of the bat's body. Now thread elastic through the other two holes on the wings and tie them to the central piece of elastic. Add a bead to the bottom string and pull it to make your bat fly!

MYSTERY MAGNETS!

Add some Scooby style to your fridge with these fab and groovy fridge magnets.

WHAT TO DO...

1 Trace the pictures of each Mystery, Inc. member from the page opposite.

2 Cut up the tracing paper picture into sections. For example, for Shaggy cut out his face, hair, t-shirt and tongue!

3 Roll out flesh colour modelling clay for his face. Lay the tracing paper section over the top and cut it out. Repeat for his light brown hair and his lime green t-shirt. Don't forget his eyes and tongue!

4 Bake it in the oven, following the instructions on the clay packet.

5 When it has cooled, use a paintbrush to add the details to Shaggy's face with black paint.

6 Glue a magnet onto the back of Shaggy's head.

Use the same method to make the entire Scooby Gang.

Your fridge will look super cool!

SECRET STORAGE!

The Mystery Machine is an essential member of the Mystery, Inc. gang! Make your own Mystery Machine to hide all your secret stuff!

1

Cut away the bottom of the larger box. Cut circles of card and glue them in place on the box to make wheels. Don't forget the spare tyre!

2

Cover the box with 2 layers of PVA glue and newspaper, padding it out at the front to make the windscreen and at the back to make the shape of the doors. Leave it to dry.

THE MYSTE
MACHI

3

Cut away the top of the smaller box and tape strips of card inside it to make compartments. Cover it with newspaper and glue and leave it to dry. Then paint it white.

YOU WILL NEED:

Two cardboard boxes - one slightly smaller than the other, scissors, PVA glue, pencil, newspaper, paints and paintbrush

4

Draw the details of the Mystery Machine onto your storage box. Start by plotting out where the windows and doors go, then work out where the flowers and crazy decorations should go. Paint it to add some colour.

5

Once it is dry, slot the smaller box underneath your Mystery Machine to make a secret hiding place for all your favourite things!

19

21

SCOOBY STRIKE!

Your friends will be bowled over by these ace Scooby skittles! They are really easy to make and you'll have hours of fun lining 'em up and knocking 'em down!

1 Blow up each of the long balloons and cover them with four layers of PVA glue and torn up newspaper. Leave them to dry until they are solid.

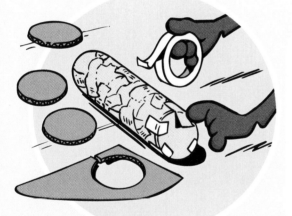

2 Once they have dried, pop the balloons. Cut the end off each balloon. Now cut six circles of card and tape one to the end of each skittle to cover the hole. Make sure that the base is flat as this is what the skittle will stand on.

3 Cover each skittle with another layer of newspaper and glue and leave to dry. The skittles need to be solid so that they don't get dented when you knock them over!

Doo

JEEPERS, THIS SURE DOES LOOK LIKE A FUN GAME TO PLAY WITH YOUR FRIENDS!

YOU WILL NEED:

Six long balloons, cardboard, paper, PVA glue, old newspapers, scissors, paints and paintbrush

4

Trace or draw each member of Mystery, Inc. on a piece of paper. Choose your favourite Scooby villain and draw him as well. Draw a number on each character as this is what you will score if you knock them over! Colour them in and cut them out.

5

Paint the six skittles and then glue a character onto the front of each one. Cover with a layer of PVA glue. Once the glue has dried, the skittles should be strong and shiny!

HOW TO PLAY!

STRIKE!

Get your friends together and take turns trying to knock the skittles down. Set the skittles up and roll a tennis ball towards them. Keep a note of the scores and award yourself an extra 20 points if you knock them all over in one go - that's a Scooby Strike!

23

DOCTOR, DOCTOR!

Jinkies, it's Mystery, Inc's old enemy, the Witch Doctor! Make this crazy money box and the Witch Doctor will scare everyone away from your pocket money!

1 Hold one of the square cardboard boxes at an angle, so that the side facing you looks diamond shaped. Cut the bottom corner off and tape it to the top of the second box. This should make the basic shape for the Witch Doctor's head and headdress.

2

Cover the whole thing with 2-3 layers of glue and torn-up newspaper. Leave it to dry.

3 Work out in pencil where the Witch Doctor's features will go. Cut a slot in his mouth for you to put your money. Cut a hole in the bottom of the moneybox, big enough for the cardboard tube to fit inside.

24

Draw a large flower shape on thick card and cut it out. Cut a hole in the middle of it, and glue it onto the bottom of the head to make the Witch Doctor's collar.

4

YOU WILL NEED:

Two cardboard boxes, old newspaper, PVA glue, a cardboard tube, thick card, scissors, tissue box, pencil, paints and paintbrush

5

Now you need to make the base of the moneybox. Glue the cardboard tube inside the tissue box. Cover the whole thing, including the gap around the tube, with newspaper and glue. The Witch Doctor's head should slot neatly on top. Finally, paint the moneybox and you are ready to save your pennies with Scooby style!

RATTLE THEM BONES!

Ruh-roh, poor Scooby is petrified of this rattling skeleton! Follow the steps to create your own skeleton spook!

1. Cut a skull shape and hip bone shape from a piece of card. Build them up with newspaper and glue to make them 3-dimensional.

2. Take a piece of black card and stick the head to the top. Cut a piece of card for the rib cage and cut some slots for the ribs.

3. Paint some uncooked pasta tubes and three drinking straws white and leave them to dry.

4. Make the arms and legs by threading pasta tubes onto string. Secure them to the card by making a hole, threading the string through and knotting it at the back.

5. To make the hands and feet, cut the straws into short pieces. Stick five pieces to a small piece of card and attach to the end of each string.

6. Add the skeleton face with black marker pen.